HANUKKAH, OH HANUKKAH

Susan L. Roth

SCHOLASTIC INC.

New York Toronto London Auckland Sydney
Mexico City New Delhi Hong Kong Buenos Aires

Hanukkah, oh Hanukkah,

come light the menorah.

Let's have a party,
we'll all dance the hora.

Gather round the table,

we'll give you a treat.

Dreidels to play with,

latkes to eat.

And while we are playing,

the candles are burning low.

One for each night,
they shed a sweet light,

HANUKKAH, OH HANUKKAH
Ha - nu - kkah, oh Ha - nu - kkah, come light the me - no - rah.
Let's have a par - ty, we'll all dance the ho - ra.
Gath - er round the ta - ble, we'll give you a treat.
Drei - dels to play with, lat - kes to eat.
And while we are play - ing, the
can - dles are burn - ing low.
One for each night, they shed a sweet light, to re -
mind us of days long a - go.
One for each night, they shed a sweet light, to re -
mind us of days long a - go.

to remind us of days long ago.

NUKKAH, OH HANUKKAH,
light the menorah . . .
HANUKKAH OH HANUKK
Susan L. Roth

One for each night,
they shed a sweet light,

to remind us of days long ago.

HANUKKAH, OH HANUKKAH

And while we are play - ing, the
can - dles are burn - ing low.
One for each night, they shed a sweet light, to re -
mind us of days long a - go.
One for each night, they shed a sweet light, to re -
mind us of days long a - go.

To Rebecca Roth's great-grandchildren, in order of appearance:

Liat, Shira, Paul, Sophia, Lena, Max, Molly, Danielle, and **Rebecca,**

and all the others yet to come.

*

Thank you to the third-grade students at Beth Tfiloh School in Baltimore, Maryland.
Many thanks also to Rona Zuckerberg, Shelly Malinow, Shoshana Krupp,
Shirley Avin, Carolyn Van Newkirk, and Zipora Schorr.
Thank you for the papers : Nobuko and Masato Kasuga, Michael Laufer, and
Jill Tarlau. And thank you to Olga R. Guartan.

*

ISBN 0-439-91435-3

12 11 10 9 8 7 6 5 4 3 2 1 6 7 8 9 10 11/0

Printed in the U.S.A. 23

First Scholastic printing, September 2006

Designed by Teresa Kietlinski

Text set in Pabst

To make these collages, I used paste, tweezers, scissors, lace,
and papers from every basket in my studio.